Spanish Nuggets

Spanish Nuggets

by Rosemary Holman

Illustrated by
Barbara Brigham

The Naylor Company
Book Publishers of the Southwest
San Antonio, Texas

Más vale tarde que nunca.

Better late than never.

Que lástima! Nadie quiere a nadie!

What a pity! Nobody likes nobody!

El trabajo hace la vida agradable.

Work makes life pleasant.

A buen hambre no hay pan duro.

For real hunger there is no stale
bread.

A E I O U, Más sabe el burro
que tú.

A E I O U, The burro knows more
than you.

En boca cerrada, no entran moscas.

In a closed mouth, no flies go in.

La rosa es roja; la violeta, azul.
El azúcar, dulce; y tambien tú.

Roses are red; violets are blue.
Sugar is sweet; and so are you.

La salud no es conocida hasta que
es perdida.

Health is not known until it is lost.

No lo hagas no lo temas.

Do not do it; do not fear it.

A mal tiempo, buena cara.

Look misfortune in the face.

No hay quinto malo.

There is no bad nickel.

Cada cabeza es un mundo.

Every head is a world.

Lo que mucho vale, mucho cuesta.

What is worth much costs much.

Más vale buena fama que cama
dorada.

A good name is worth more than
a gilded bed.

Cada chango a su mecate.

Each monkey to his rope.

El perro que ladra, no muerde.

A barking dog never bites.

No desdenes consejos aunque seas
sabio y viejo.

Do not disdain advice although
you are wise and old.

No hay miel sin hiel.

There is no honey without gall.

Quien busca, halla.

He who seeks, finds.

Quien a buen árbol se arrima,
buena sombra le cobija.

When one gets under a good tree,
a good shade covers him.

Quien mal anda, mal acaba.

He who acts badly, ends badly.

Estoy perdido sin fé.

I am lost without faith.

Quien mucho duerme, poco
   aprende.

He who sleeps much, learns little.

No hay tiempo como el presente.

There is no time like the present.

Quien no se aventura, no pasa el
mar.

He who does not venture does not
cross the sea.

En cada tierra su uso, y en cada
casa su costumbre.

In every land its usage, and in every
house its custom.

PICASSO

A Biography by
ELIZABETH RIPLEY

J. B. LIPPINCOTT COMPANY Philadelphia · New York

J B
P

For
H. P. B.

Copyright © 1959
By Elizabeth Ripley
Lithographed in the United States of America
By Affiliated Lithographers
Library of Congress Catalog Card Number 59-12358

ILLUSTRATIONS

Eɪɢʜᴛ-ʏᴇᴀʀ-ᴏʟᴅ Pablo Ruiz glared reproachfully at his father, turned on his heel and strode into the chilly school building. All morning he sat at his desk watching the clock behind the teacher, and when the hands pointed to twelve he ran out into the sunny courtyard where his father was waiting. School was a nightmare, he told Don José Ruiz. He had learned nothing, absolutely nothing.

Every morning Don José dragged his son to school and each time the schoolroom door closed behind him, Pablo felt terribly alone. One morning he refused to leave the house without a pet pigeon to keep him company. Holding the warm bird close to his chest he felt less lonely, but he could not concentrate on what the teacher was saying. His dark eyes seemed to burn into the pages of the open book in front of him, as he imagined how he could decorate the margins with pictures of the bullfight he had seen with his father on Sunday.

In the afternoons Pablo loved to amuse his little sister by drawing charging bulls and galloping horsemen. Once he painted a picture of a bullfighter on horseback, dressed in a bright yellow jacket. The little girl watched, fascinated, while he blocked in the heads of a woman and two men in the grandstand. Grasping a nail in her tiny fist, she leaned over the wooden panel and clumsily pierced five holes in the spots where she thought the eyes should be.

Pablo was ten years old when his father moved his family to Corunna on the coast of Spain. He was overjoyed that he would never see the school in Malaga again, and that he was to study in the art school where his father was teaching. There he painted still-life pictures of fruit and flowers and dead pigeons which Don José arranged for him in the studio. He worked so quickly and easily that soon Don José realized that his son was becoming a better painter than his father. Then one day in 1895, Don José handed his paints and brushes to his fourteen-year-old son, for he had decided he would never paint again.

BULLFIGHTER ON HORSEBACK

1889
Collection Picasso
Photo Giraudon

Pablo was fifteen years old when Don José moved his family to Barcelona. He told his father that he wanted to enter the art school where Don José was teaching. In just one day he completed the examinations which older students labored on for a whole month. The directors were staggered by his skill, and awarded him first prize. Don José, overjoyed at his son's success, rented a little studio where he could work undisturbed. With amazing speed Pablo painted pictures of subjects chosen by his father. Blond, bearded Don José insisted on posing as the doctor in one painting which he named *Science and Charity*. When the painting won first prize in Madrid, he decided that Pablo should finish his studies in that city.

Once again Pablo completed the examinations in a few hours and was admitted with honors to Spain's most important art school. But Pablo soon gave up going to classes. Instead he roamed the windy streets, observing everything and making hundreds of drawings in his cold little room. He was often hungry that winter in Madrid and in the spring he fell ill. The fever left him so weak that he decided to spend the summer in the country. There he learned how to milk a cow, cook rice, and take care of a horse. Eight months later a healthy Pablo returned to Barcelona.

He hired a shabby room over a corset factory and painted day and night. He drew portraits of everyone he knew—his father, mother and sister and of the artists and writers he met at the café of the Four Cats. Jaime Sabartès, a quiet young poet with thick glasses, called on him one day and found him "lost under a heap of drawings," which were signed "P. Ruiz Picasso," for Pablo had decided to call himself by his mother's maiden name.

The artists at the Four Cats urged Pablo to visit Paris. Pablo's mother, confident of her son's genius, persuaded Don José to give him the money for the trip. One October day in 1900, nineteen-year-old Pablo and two friends boarded a train for France.

LA MALADE

1897
Study for *Science and Charity*
Collection, the artist's family

Pablo followed his friends up six winding flights of stairs to the studio which a Spanish friend had loaned them. He did not stop to unpack his bags, for he was eager to look at Paris. He did not understand a word of French, but his keen eyes took in everything about him.

Pablo filled his letters to Barcelona with sketches of what he saw —a mongrel dog he had adopted, apache men in visor caps, and coarse looking women, their faces smeared with make-up. He studied people in cafés and watched the shifting lights and colors in dance halls at night. He painted a picture of stylishly dressed couples dancing in one of Paris' famous night clubs.

One afternoon a young woman art dealer climbed the stairs to Pablo's studio. A rich Spaniard named Maynac living in Paris had told her about the young painter. Terrified by the artist's fierce eyes, Berthe Weill quickly picked out three bullfighting scenes for her gallery. Maynac was so impressed by this success, that he offered Pablo a small salary to paint pictures which Maynac could sell to Paris art dealers. Pablo was delighted that he no longer needed to ask his father for money, and because he was free to paint wherever he wished he decided to return to Spain for Christmas.

As soon as the holidays were over Pablo set off for Madrid where he rented an unheated attic room.

"Never have I been so cold," he told Jaime Sabartès later. He was hungry, too, but he painted constantly. A young writer asked him to help him start an art magazine.

"*Young Art* will be a sincere paper," wrote Picasso in the first issue. But *Young Art* did not sell and in May, Pablo returned to Barcelona where his friends persuaded him to show his pictures. Hastily he picked out glowing pastels for Barcelona's biggest gallery. He did not stay to read the critics' praises, for late in May 1901, Pablo and his friend were on their way to Paris.

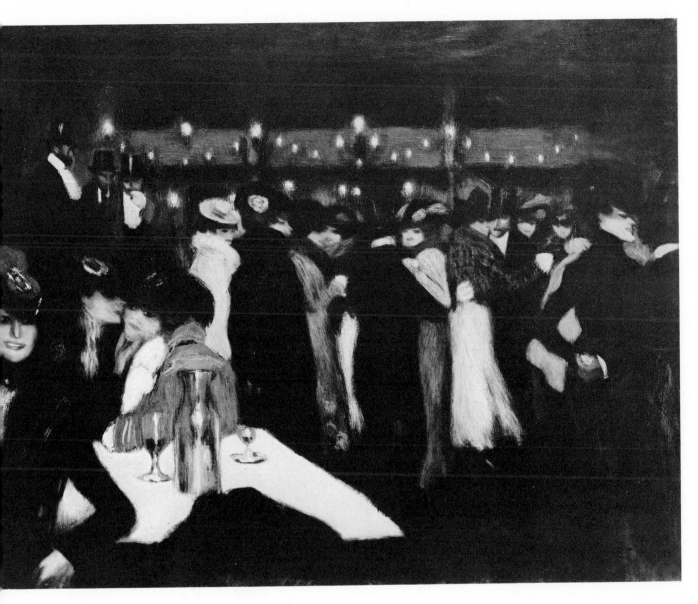

LE MOULIN DE LA GALETTE

1900
Collection of Mr. and Mrs. Justin K. Thannhauser, New York

Maynac was waiting for Pablo in the studio which he had rented for him. The important art dealer Vollard was anxious to see Picasso's paintings, Maynac told him. Pablo put on his broad-brimmed hat, picked up his bulging portfolios and set off with Maynac to the gallery.

Vollard watched amazed as Picasso showed him pictures of toreadors, Spanish street scenes, bright flower paintings and somber canvases of couples embracing. Although this stocky young Spaniard with dark hair falling over his forehead and eyes like burning coals could not talk to him in French, he spoke brilliantly in his pictures. Vollard told Maynac he wanted to exhibit Picasso's work.

Three weeks later many Parisians saw Picasso's paintings for the first time. Some were confused by the different types of pictures, but one young poet named Max Jacob was so impressed that he came to Picasso's studio to congratulate him. They did not talk each other's language, but painter and poet shook hands vigorously, and from that day they became warm friends. In the evenings Jacob joined Picasso and his friends in the cobwebby back room of a café which the owner reserved for them. Soon Pablo was able to talk to Max in broken French. The "Bande Picasso" often returned to Pablo's studio at night where they slept on the floor with canvases propped against them to keep themselves warm.

Maynac complained that Picasso used the studio as a home for his friends and that he painted pictures of sad clowns in a blue light which the dealers would not buy. Worn out by constant arguments Picasso decided to return to Barcelona. But after a few months he began to miss his friends in Paris, so in the fall he returned to France.

In the little room which he shared with Max Jacob, Picasso painted all night and slept in the one bed during the day while Jacob worked in a store. Too poor to buy coal he burned drawing after drawing to keep himself from freezing. He longed to return to sunny Barcelona, but he didn't have enough money for the fare. Then one day he sold a painting for the price of a ticket to Spain.

SELF PORTRAIT

1901
Private Collection, New York

"I haven't written for a long time," Picasso wrote to Max Jacob. "It is not because I don't think of you, but because I am working, and when I am working I amuse myself."

Every day Picasso joined his friends at the Four Cats, but when the conversation bored him he got up abruptly saying to Sabartès, "Are you coming?"

"What fools," he would remark to his friend as they walked in the direction of the studio which he shared with another artist. Sometimes when Pablo became ill-humored he asked Sabertès to pose for him, and when the portrait of his friend was finished, Picasso's mood had changed.

Everywhere in the studio Sabartès saw blue pictures of elongated drooping figures—an emaciated old man bent over his guitar, a sad dark-eyed boy pressed close to the side of an old Jew, and a ragged man and woman shivering with cold, standing by the seaside.

"I'll get used to them," Sabartès said, when he saw the melancholy pictures for the first time.

In the same blue light Picasso painted a blind man seated at a table. One hand held a piece of bread and the long sensitive fingers of the other hand reached toward a jug of wine. To Picasso, whose life depended on his eyes, blindness seemed the cruelest of sufferings.

The studio where Picasso worked became so filled with paintings that finally Pablo decided to rent one of his own. For the first time he was able to work undisturbed and to lock the door on his canvases when he joined his friends at the Four Cats. He loved to feel the heavy key in his pocket.

Three months after Picasso had moved into his private studio he learned that a Paris art gallery was showing some of his pictures. At twenty-five he was becoming known to French dealers. Encouraged by this news Pablo decided to return to Paris.

BLIND MAN'S MEAL

1903
The Metropolitan Museum of Art, New York
Gift of Mr. and Mrs. Ira Haupt

In Paris, halfway up the hill named Montmartre, stood a rickety wooden building which people had named The Laundry Boat, or *Bateau Lavoir*. Here Picasso rented a studio furnished with a mattress, a table, an old iron stove and one chair. At the foot of the hill was a cabaret called *Le Lapin Agile*. Freddy, the genial owner, always saved a special table in the garden for "his children," as he called the artists and writers who gathered there. Here Picasso would sit, pipe in mouth, talking in poor French with admiring friends. He loved Freddy's mangey donkey that trotted about the garden and the pet crow which followed Freddy's daughter from table to table. He painted a picture of the girl tenderly caressing the crow with her long fingers.

When Picasso left *Le Lapin Agile* late at night, friends often followed him up the hill to the *Bateau Lavoir*. Sometimes he walked silently thinking of the pictures he would paint. One night, annoyed by a group of artists who were carrying him home in triumph, he suddenly pulled out a revolver and fired it in the air. In terror his admirers fled.

As soon as he returned from the café, Picasso locked himself in his studio and worked until morning. All about the room were canvases of hungry looking people with gray faces—melancholy Harlequins, angular actors, acrobats and jugglers, for Picasso went to the circus whenever he could afford it. When the people of Montmartre were on their way to work, Picasso would fling himself on his mattress and sleep until evening.

One afternoon a man and woman wearing sandals and brown velvet robes knocked on Picasso's door. Pablo was immediately attracted by the mannish looking woman who introduced herself as Gertrude Stein. This wealthy American writer and her brother had bought one of Picasso's paintings and wanted to see more of them. Before she left, Gertrude Stein offered Picasso a large price for several of his canvases.

WOMAN WITH CROW

1904
The Toledo Museum of Art
Gift of Edward Drummond Libbey

Picasso could now afford to go to the circus as often as he wished. His keen eyes followed every movement of the graceful acrobats and skilled jugglers. He laughed uproariously at the clowns, and when the performance was over he talked to them for hours in the bar.

Picasso's days of desperate poverty were over. He no longer had to live on beans cooked on his iron stove. The half-starved people of the "blue period" had disappeared from his canvases. In tones of rose and tan he painted wistful acrobats in lonely settings.

One huge picture showed a family of acrobats standing on a beach against a timeless background of sky and sea.

Picasso began to work in the daytime so that he would be awake when people called to buy his paintings. In the evenings when he was not at the circus, artists and writers would climb the creaking stairs of the *Bateau Lavoir*. Here in Pablo's attic studio, freezing cold in winter and stiflingly hot in summer, the friends talked, laughed, drank and sang until late at night; then the next day Pablo would be hard at work. Dressed in a dirty sweat shirt and baggy trousers, he received art dealers and wealthy customers.

"Monsieur Picasso, you can open. It is a serious visitor," the door-keeper would call through the studio door, for she had learned to recognize the people who had come to buy paintings.

Every Saturday evening Picasso put on a fresh shirt, necktie and clean suit and set off across the river to the home of Gertrude and Leo Stein. In their big house filled with paintings, the Steins entertained well-known artists and writers.

Picasso was delighted when Gertrude Stein agreed to sit for her portrait. Ever since he had met her he had longed to paint her strong intelligent face. So one afternoon Gertrude Stein boarded an omnibus which took her across the river to the *Bateau Lavoir*.

FAMILY OF ACROBATS AT SEASIDE

1905
National Gallery, Washington
Chester Dale Collection

In a few hours Picasso painted a striking likeness of Gertrude Stein, but he grumbled that he was not satisfied. Eighty times she returned to the *Bateau Lavoir* so that Picasso could finish her portrait.

"When I look at you I don't see you," he growled one day as he angrily wiped out the whole head. Exasperated that he could not paint her as he saw her, he left the unfinished portrait standing against the wall.

One spring day the art dealer Vollard called at the *Bateau Lavoir*. He had not visited Picasso for some time, for he complained he could not sell Picasso's blue paintings. All about the studio were rose-colored pictures of Harlequins and acrobats. When Vollard left a few hours later, he had bought thirty of these canvases at a big price. Picasso, delighted that he could now realize his dream of a trip to Spain, packed up his bags and boarded a train for Barcelona. After a short visit with his family, he set off for the little mountain village of Gosol.

Picasso was happy that summer. He hunted, drank and played games with the peasants, and he painted with renewed vigor.

He had left the wistful acrobats behind him. Here in the clear mountain air he saw everything in a different light. He painted pictures of peasants—short stocky figures which looked as if they were built out of blocks.

The unfinished portrait of Gertrude Stein was still leaning against the wall of his studio the day Picasso returned to the *Bateau Lavoir*. He did not stop to unpack his bags but set the canvas on his easel and slashed in a portrait of his friend—hands resting on her lap, her mask-like face thrust forward and her eyes slightly squinting as if she were listening intently.

"Does the portrait look like me?" Gertrude Stein asked surprised, when she saw it for the first time.

"It will one day," was Picasso's quick reply.

"For me it is I," Gertrude Stein wrote, after the portrait had hung in her house for many years. "It is the only reproduction of me which is always I for me."

18

GERTRUDE STEIN

1906
The Metropolitan Museum of Art, New York
Bequest of Gertrude Stein

A thin, elegantly dressed man climbed the stairs to Picasso's studio one day in 1906. This young German who had just opened a tiny art gallery in Paris was eager to meet the twenty-five-year-old artist whose pictures of Harlequins and acrobats were so popular. Henry Kahnweiler was startled by the short, thick-set man wearing rumpled trousers and muddy shoes, who opened the door brusquely when he knocked; but as soon as he looked at the canvases scattered about the disorderly studio, he knew that he wanted to hang them in his gallery.

Every time Kahnweiler returned to the *Bateau Lavoir* he bought more paintings. Picasso stuffed the franc notes into his wallet, placed it in his pocket and fastened the opening with a big safety pin.

In the spring of 1907, Picasso showed Kahnweiler some drawings of distorted angular nude figures with mask-like faces and big oval eyes. His eyes blazed as he told Kahnweiler that he was finding a new way to picture the rounded forms of the human figure without using shading or curved lines. This was the agonizing task he was undertaking.

Every day he shut himself in his studio and when he emerged his expression was tortured. Why didn't he paint more Harlequins and acrobats which Vollard could sell, his friends wondered.

"How could I be sure I was doing the right thing against everyone else's reason?" he said later. "I didn't know, but I couldn't do otherwise."

"Has Picasso gone crazy?" one friend asked when he looked at the painting on which he had worked all summer. His artist friend Georges Braque did not like it or understand it, and Vollard shook his head. Kahnweiler, who saw what Picasso was trying to show in this startling canvas of five barbaric looking nudes, wanted to buy the picture. But Picasso said it was not finished.

The painting stayed in Picasso's studio for many years. A friend named it *The Ladies of Avignon,* for a street in Barcelona where Picasso had lived. But Picasso didn't like the title.

"*Les Demoiselles d'Avignon*—how that name irritates me!" he growled.

LES DEMOISELLES D'AVIGNON

1907
Museum of Modern Art, New York

Gertrude Stein's guests were horrified by the three landscape pictures which she hung in her living room in the fall of 1909. Picasso had painted them that summer in a little mountain town in Spain, she told her friends. Under the strong sun he saw everything in a new way. In this painting the hillside, the factory and the reservoir seemed to be built out of transparent cubes, cones and cylinders.

Picasso did not go back to the *Bateau Lavoir* when he returned to Paris that fall. He moved his few pieces of furniture, his dog, his three Siamese cats and his pet monkey into a big apartment. A friend loaned him a sofa and a piano, and wherever he went he bought pieces of furniture—a big iron bedstead for his bedroom, a huge sideboard for his dining room, and one day he bought a little organ which puffed out incense when it was pumped. A maid dressed in a white apron served him his meals, but she knew she must never sweep his cluttered studio. Scattered all about the big room were African masks, pieces of tapestry, guitars, mandolins, and cartons filled with odds and ends he had collected. Here Picasso worked every afternoon until it grew dark. He painted the human figure in the same new way he had painted the landscapes in Spain. The faces were empty blocks and the bodies looked as if they had been built out of metal cubes.

During the spring and summer of 1910, he painted portraits of his friends—the art dealer Vollard, his artist friend Braque, and Henry Kahnweiler who came twenty times to sit for his portrait. He did not construct these faces out of blocks, for once again Picasso had started to see things in a new way. The faces appeared to be broken up into little flat shapes in shades of browns and grays. These shapes he put together "with the technique of a great surgeon," a critic wrote.

People looking at these portraits for the first time saw only a jumble of pieces, but soon they realized that from this abstract pattern emerged the likeness of the sitter.

HENRY KAHNWEILER

Wherever Picasso went people gathered around him, asking questions about his latest paintings.

"Why do people always want to explain a picture?" Picasso once asked. "Why not explain a bird song, the night, a flower?"

So irritated did he become when people asked him to express his thoughts, that he often sat silently through a whole meal. He was happier dining in his apartment with only his pet monkey to share his food. Visitors to his studio received brusque answers when they asked him to explain his pictures. He longed to get away from people, so in the summer of 1911 he and his friend Braque set off for a village in the south of France.

The two artists returned to Paris in the fall with trunks full of canvases. Braque, like Picasso, had been working on the problem of breaking up forms into angular shapes. Braque's landscapes looked as if they were "made out of little cubes," the painter Matisse remarked. And so people used the word "cubism" to describe this style of painting.

Cubism shocked many people, and others could not understand it, but more and more artists began to express themselves in this new way. They painted still lifes like those Braque and Picasso had brought back from the south of France. They used only the objects which were in their studio—a violin, a guitar, a playing card, a pipe. Parts of these objects were easy to recognize, while other parts were broken up into transparent shapes which overlapped and fitted together in pleasing patterns. Usually a few letters carefully copied from a newspaper heading stood out boldly somewhere in the composition.

Picasso tried pasting real objects on his paintings. His pockets bulged with bits of cloth, buttons, strings and pebbles which he glued on his canvases to make interesting textures. Because the French word for glue is *colle,* someone named these pictures "collages."

GLASS AND BOTTLE OF BASS

1913
Pasted papers with sawdust on cardboard
Collection Mrs. George Henry Warren
Photograph courtesy of the Museum of Modern Art, New York

"You can paint with anything you like," a critic wrote about the Cubist artists, " with pipes, postage stamps . . . or newspaper."

Sometimes Picasso mixed plaster with paint and molded the colored mixture on his canvas so that the picture looked more like a piece of sculpture than a painting. He stirred sand and sawdust into his colors when he wanted to give an effect of roughness, and sometimes, in order to show a granulated surface, he decorated that part with brightly colored dots. He kept cans of enamel house paint beside him on the floor and used the pure shiny colors on his canvases.

In the summer of 1914, Picasso, Braque and the painter Derain set off for Avignon in the south of France. There Picasso painted richly colored still lifes of bottles, glasses and guitars. He was working on one of his gayest pictures one August day when he learned the news that Germany had declared war on France. Angered by this unjust attack on the country which he had come to love, Picasso picked up his brush and wrote on one of the glasses in his picture *VIVE LA* (long live), and underneath he painted two crossed flags, the tricolor of France.

"I see very few people," Picasso wrote when he returned to Paris in the fall. Braque and Derain were in the French army, Gertrude Stein was in England, and Kahnweiler, not wishing to return to his home in Germany, had fled to Switzerland.

His good friend Max Jacob was still in Paris. Picasso drew a portrait of the little bald headed poet, which looked exactly like him.

"I want to see if I can paint like everyone else," he told Jacob. He drew a portrait of Vollard, a perfect likeness of the round-faced bearded art dealer, and he made realistic drawings of Harlequins. Critics rejoiced that he had given up the cubist style of painting, but Picasso often used these drawings as studies for a cubist picture, breaking up the forms in his classically drawn Harlequins and putting them together again in gaily colored patterns.

VIVE LA . . .

1914
Courtesy of the Sidney Janis Gallery, New York

One day Picasso met a young poet whose sharp features reminded him so much of a Harlequin, that he asked if he could paint his portrait. Picasso's picture of Jean Cocteau was a cubist portrait which did not look at all like Cocteau, but from that day painter and poet became fast friends.

Cocteau persuaded Picasso to design sets and costumes for a ballet he had written and which a Russian company was rehearsing in Rome. Intrigued by this ballet—about two acrobats, a juggler and a little American girl—Picasso set to work making a model set. Then in February 1917, he and Cocteau boarded a train for Rome.

While Cocteau watched rehearsals in a café basement, Picasso sat at a table, drawing grotesque designs for costumes which looked as if they had been made out of pieces of scenery. Cocteau realized that these towering "stage set characters," that Picasso called "The Managers," would make the dancers look like puppets, so he added the new characters to his ballet.

Picasso began immediately to build the costumes out of cardboard, pipes and jointed wood panels. The New York Manager, wearing cowboy boots and a stove pipe hat carried a megaphone in his hand. A cardboard skyscraper was attached to his shoulder.

"In the evenings we walked in the moonlight with the dancers," Cocteau told a friend. Picasso, charmed by the grace and dignity of one of the ballerinas, soon fell in love with beautiful Olga Khoklova.

One May evening, artists in overalls and elegantly dressed ladies and gentlemen gathered at a Paris theater to see the first performance of *Parade*. As Picasso's gay curtain of Harlequins, circus riders and guitarists rose, two machine-like figures, ten feet high, stamped across the stage. The audience hissed furiously.

"Every morning I receive new insults," Cocteau said when he read the reviews of *Parade*. But Picasso paid little attention to the critics. When the theater closed, a few days later, he and Olga Khoklova set off for Spain.

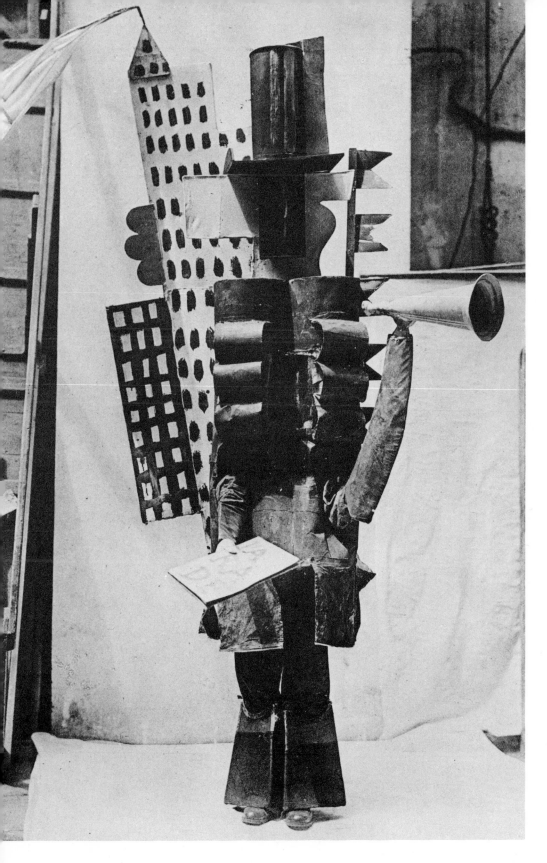

THE NEW YORK MANAGER

1917
Costume design for *PARADE*

Picasso showed Olga the sights of Madrid, then took her to Barcelona to introduce her to his family. There he painted her portrait wearing a white lace mantilla. The picture was a photographic likeness of the girl he planned to marry. Before he and Olga returned to Paris he gave the portrait to his mother.

Olga and Pablo were married at the Russian Church in Paris one July day in 1918. Cocteau and Max Jacob were Picasso's witnesses at the long, pompous ceremony.

Picasso at thirty-seven started to lead a more settled life. In November the war with Germany was over. Pablo's friends returned to Paris. He and Olga entertained them in their big apartment in a fashionable district of the city. When he went out his hair was carefully combed, a gold watch chain was fastened in his buttonhole, and a white handkerchief was neatly folded in his jacket pocket. He painted realistic pictures of Pierrots and meticulous still lifes of things in his home.

He painted a portrait of Olga wearing a net dress. Her evenly waved hair framed her classical face. One hand rested on the back of a chair which was covered with a flowered tapestry. In the other hand she held a fan.

"A typical society portrait," a cubist artist remarked scornfully, when he saw the picture.

MADAME OLGA PICASSO

One July evening in 1919, an audience gathered at a London theater to see the opening of a ballet called *The Three Cornered Hat*. Undaunted by the failure of *Parade,* Picasso had agreed to design the sets and costumes for this ballet about Spain. The curtain showed a balcony of a bull ring where gentlemen in capes and sombreros talked with ladies in mantillas. The set suggested a Spanish mountain village. The peasant costumes were decorated with stripes and spirals of colored cloth and braid. Then, just before the curtain rose, Picasso painted dazzling patterns on some of the ballerina's dresses. There were no towering cubist figures to shock the audience that night. Critics and spectators applauded loudly.

Picasso did not stay long in London. A few days after the opening of *The Three Cornered Hat,* he joined Olga in fashionable St. Raphael on the coast of France. From their window they looked out on clear blue sky and sea. On a table in front of the open window Picasso arranged still lifes of books, jugs and guitars. He painted watercolors of these still lifes in pastel tones, breaking up the objects into cubist shapes and placing them against a background of serene blue sky and sea.

These were the watercolors which a dealer exhibited when Picasso returned to Paris in the fall. Once again Picasso's new pictures surprised the critics, for in these paintings of the open window at St. Raphael, cubism and realism had been combined.

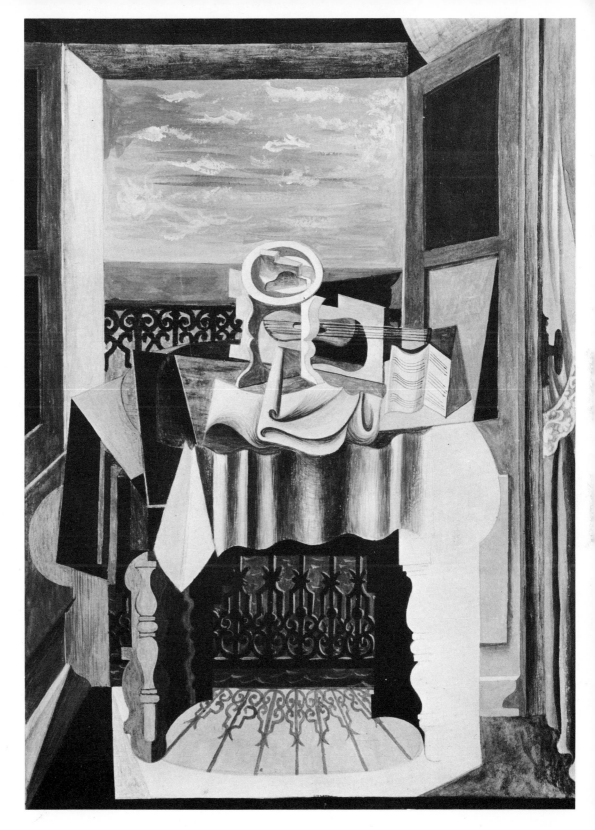

THE WINDOW

1919
Private collection, New York
Photograph courtesy of the Museum of Modern Art, New York

The next spring Picasso, longing for sun and sea set off with Olga for the south of France. The landscape of Juan-les-Pins was just as he had imagined it, and he painted a cubist picture of the white houses with red roofs and blue shutters surrounded by gaily colored gardens. He painted still lifes of guitars and mandolins on a table, and pictures of women bathers on the beach. Some were cubist bathers, mechanical figures in striped bathing suits, and some were distorted nudes with tiny heads and enormous legs. Many of Picasso's women bathers were heavy rock-like figures which suggested Greek and Roman statues. The serenity of Picasso's life that summer seemed to be reflected in these reposeful giants.

The next winter Paul Picasso was born. Pablo was overjoyed. He sketched his baby son when he was only two weeks old. He sketched him again a few weeks later. The miracle of the growing child fascinated him. Almost every month he made realistic drawings of his little son.

In the spring Picasso rented a country house in nearby Fountainbleau, and there he painted pictures of a mother with her child. The mother had Olga's features and the baby looked like Paul.

Picasso drew and painted constantly during that peaceful summer. He made drawings of his vine-covered house and the formal parlor with Olga seated at the piano. Walking through the forest he caught "an indigestion of green," he told a friend, so, in order to cure himself he painted woodland scenes.

One day he started a picture of three monumental antique women at a fountain and the next day he was working on an enormous cubist composition of three masked musicians.

When Picasso returned to Paris in the fall he brought with him ten different paintings of *Three Women at a Fountain,* and two enormous canvases of *The Three Musicians.*

MOTHER AND CHILD

1921
Courtesy of the Art Institute of Chicago

A Pierrot, a Harlequin and a monk—these were the three masked musicians in Picasso's big cubist paintings. In one picture these more than life-size figures, composed out of flat geometric shapes, were painted in bright shiny colors against a warm brown background. The Pierrot dressed in white played a clarinet, the Harlequin, wearing a costume of red and yellow checks, was playing a guitar and the monk, wearing black robes, held a sheet of music.

Picasso's other canvas of the three musicians was a gayer picture. The geometric shapes were less severe, the background lighter. Pierrot sat in the center, the sheet of music on a table in front of him, and Harlequin, sitting on the left, played a violin.

THE THREE MUSICIANS

1921
Philadelphia Museum of Art

Picasso never tired of drawing pictures of his son. He drew him in his mother's arms and sitting on her lap. He painted him standing unsteadily on little fat legs, holding a toy horse. He sketched him as he ate, and while he was playing on the beach.

He copied a photograph of his two-year-old son, dressed in a white suit and cap, sitting astride a donkey. He painted him again, bent over a little desk, intent on the picture he was drawing.

When Paul was three his father painted him wearing the blue and yellow costume of a Harlequin. The serious little boy with big brown eyes sat shyly on the edge of a large upholstered chair. The next year, a taller, more confident Paul posed in a white Pierrot's suit.

That same year Picasso spent many hours watching rehearsals of the Russian ballet. His penetrating eyes followed every movement of the dancers and with one continuous line of his pen he sketched each graceful motion. Picasso was finding a new way to express the human figure in action.

PAUL AS HARLEQUIN

That summer Picasso painted a startling picture of three dancers. The dislocated figures painted in loud colors, their forms outlined by distorted shadows, danced in front of an open window. The dancer in the middle flung her arms wildly in the air. Her one eye, placed perpendicularly in her rectangular face, seemed to exaggerate the violence of her movement. The dancer on the left was made out of pieces cut in jagged shapes which gave an effect of frenzied action.

The classical women with Olga's features disappeared from Picasso's canvases. He continued to paint bathers, but they were monstrous creatures with tiny heads, long necks and arms and legs like tree trunks. Some, made out of bone-like forms, looked like distorted skeletons. Picasso longed to build these figures in clay, but there was no room in his over-crowded studio to work on pieces of sculpture.

Instead he sketched designs for enormous monuments which he imagined set up along the coast of France.

"I have to be content with painting them," he told Kahnweiler, "because nobody will give me a commission for one."

THREE DANCERS

1925
The Artist
Copyright by SPADEM Paris

Each year Picasso's apartment became more crowded. The walls of every room were hung with paintings, and the tables and the mantlepieces were covered with pieces of sculpture. Drawings and etchings were piled high on every table in his studio. Framed and unframed canvases rested on easels, the backs of chairs or in stacks against the walls.

Over and over the same subjects appeared in Picasso's canvases, but every time he painted these subjects he saw them in a different way. He never tired of picturing still lifes on a table. Some of them were painted in vivid transparent colors which were bound together by curving black outlines, so that the pictures looked like stained-glass windows. Sometimes the curves twisted and turned so violently that the objects which they outlined seemed to come to life. Picasso pulled one of these still lifes from a pile of canvases one day and showed it to a friend. The yellow jug seemed to be thrusting out its chest, the plums looked as if they were rolling off the dish. Even the wall in the background appeared to be moving. Picasso turned to his friend, his black eyes smiling. "There's a *still* life for you!" he exclaimed.

In the spring of 1937 Picasso bought a big estate in Boisgeloup, not far from Paris. Into the rooms of this spacious house he moved truck loads of paintings, drawings and engravings. He opened the doors of the stables letting in light so that he could use them as a sculptor's studio.

Fifty-year-old Picasso, now rich and famous, had found room at last to work in clay and plaster.

STILL LIFE ON TABLE

In his stable studio Picasso modeled monumental women's heads, three feet high. One of these, cast in gilded bronze, had the classical features of a young woman Picasso had met in Paris. Attracted by her calm blond beauty, he sculptured her many times. Some of these women's heads had long thin necks, big noses and bulging eyes; but they were all majestic heads, inspired by the beautiful woman whom Picasso loved. Picasso painted pictures of her as she slept in an armchair, her relaxed figure outlined in big rhythmic curves. Over and over he painted this sleeping woman—and then suddenly one day, Picasso gave up painting.

"You can imagine what has happened and what is in store for me," he wrote despairingly to Sabartès. Olga and Paul had left his home for ever. Pablo begged his friend to visit him in Paris.

Picasso seemed restless and depressed, Sabartès thought, when he arrived in Paris one November day in 1935.

"He doesn't go his studio any more," his friend wrote. "Each picture reminds him of something in the past."

"This can't go on!" Pablo groaned one day. "I *must* do something else!" And so Picasso began to write.

Shutting himself in his room he wrote poems in different colored pencils, so that the pages of his notebook were decorated with gay stripes.

Sabartès tried to protect Picasso from the throngs of people who called at his home.

"If only people would leave me alone," he would growl. Finally, in despair, he decided to leave Paris.

A few weeks later he returned from the south of France with a trunk full of drawings. He was ready to work again, he told Sabartès. He decided to illustrate a book on natural history, which he had promised Vollard many years before. Picasso worked with enthusiasm, for he loved animals. He made thirty-one different drawings, at least one a day. Because he saw each animal so clearly in his mind he was able to draw it as if it had been in front of him.

THE TOAD

1936
Aquatint for Buffon's *Natural History*
Collection Museum of Modern Art

In the summer of 1936, civil war broke out in Spain. Angered by the news that the dictator General Franco was leading a revolt against the government of Spain, Picasso sent money to help the army of the Republic. He was so moved by tales of suffering in his country, that he sold some of his favorite canvases to buy milk for starving children.

During this tragic year the Spanish government asked Picasso to decorate a wall of the pavilion which it was building for the Paris exposition. Picasso rented a vast studio, big enough to hold an enormous canvas, but when spring came he had not even started on the picture.

Then one April day in 1937, he learned that the little Spanish town of Guernica had been destroyed. For three hours German planes flying for Franco had dropped bombs on the helpless town. Two thousand innocent people had been killed. Picasso's dark eyes blazed when he read the news. He picked up a pencil and started to draw. In ten days he made hundreds of drawings of wounded horses, dying riders and shrieking women as he worked out a composition for a painting. One month later Picasso's huge canvas, *Guernica,* was hung in the Spanish pavilion.

Visitors to the exposition were stunned by the power of the picture. It was a scene of violent tragedy, painted in black, grey and white. On the right a woman, shrieking in agony, fell from a burning building. Another lunged forward, begging to be saved. A woman holding a lamp leaned from a window, crying out in horror. In the center a wounded horse howled in anguish, while under its feet lay a shattered rider clutching a broken sword. On the left a mother holding her child cried out in despair. Over her towered a snorting bull. The hatred which Picasso felt for oppression and brute force was expressed in the face of this cruel beast. The wounded horse, the fallen rider and the shrieking women were all helpless victims of the bull's attack. The only sign of life in this scene of devastation was the flower growing from the dead horseman's hand.

GUERNICA

1937
The Artist
Courtesy of the Museum of Modern Art

Picasso was exhausted after a month of furious work. He packed paints and canvases into his big car and with his Afghan hound, Kazbek, set off for the south of France. Still haunted by the horrors of Guernica, he painted pictures of weeping women. At the same time he painted portraits in bright colors; the sitters were decorated with brilliant stripes, checks and spirals so that they looked like pieces of embroidery. Others looked like scarecrows, with wood shavings for hair, eyebrows of pine needles and fingers like carrots.

Every summer Picasso returned to the south of France. He painted constantly, trying to ignore the threats of war in Europe. Then in the fall of 1939, news came that France and Germany were at war.

"Just as I was beginning to work," Picasso growled. Rolling up the enormous canvas he had started in Antibes, he and Sabartès returned to Paris. He began frantically to pack the paintings in his studio. Three days later Parisians learned that Hitler's army had marched into Poland. That night, Picasso, Kazbek and Sabartès were driving south towards Royan.

In an apartment filled with furniture, Picasso started to work. Bent over a chair which he used as an easel, he painted portraits of his friends.

When Sabartès called at the apartment one afternoon he saw a startling portrait of himself wearing a ruff and a plumed hat. The face was twisted violently, the mouth pushed to the left, the eyes and chin to the right and the nose placed in profile. Even the glasses were upside down.

"It doesn't please you?" Picasso asked, smiling.

"You know I never exclaim," his friend replied, but he knew that he would understand the picture later.

"It has the characteristics of my face," he thought to himself as he walked home that night, "and only the most essential."

JAIME SABARTÈS

October 22, 1939
Collection Sabartès, Paris
Copyright by SPADEM Paris

In his crowded room, using a chair seat for a palette and brushes which he made himself, Picasso continued to paint portraits of his friends. As the war news grew more alarming their features became more twisted. In May the German army marched into France. A few weeks later Picasso watched from his window as Hitler's grey-uniformed soldiers paraded down the street.

"They think they're more intelligent," he said to Sabartès, "perhaps they are . . . but in any case we paint better."

Letters poured in from friends who urged Picasso to seek safety in America, but Pablo preferred to stay in France. That fall he packed up his paintings and returned to Paris.

"All that is left for me is to fight for food, see my friends and wait for liberty," he said.

Hitler's ambassador visited Picasso's frigid studio one day. He offered him coal, but Picasso said he preferred to freeze with the Parisians. As the ambassador turned to go a photograph of *Guernica* caught his eye.

"So you did that, Monsieur Picasso?" he asked surprised.

"NO," snapped Picasso, his dark eyes burning as he thought of the town destroyed by German bombs, *"you* did it!"

Picasso, tortured by chilblains, often found it hard to hold a brush, but he painted constantly. The Nazis forbade him to show his pictures.

"But," he said, "it wasn't the moment for a creative man to fall down."

He painted seated women with violently twisted features. Intrigued by the subject of childhood he painted pictures of babies. He had no models for the grotesque looking children. One picture showed a child taking his first steps. Its staring eyes and twisted mouth expressed the concentration and sense of triumph a child feels when it starts to walk alone. The more than life-size figure seemed to fill the entire canvas, but a few days later, Picasso decided to paint in the figure of a mother, anxiously bending over her child.

FIRST STEPS

1943
Courtesy of Yale University Art Gallery

Picasso picked up an old gas pipe from the floor of his studio. The straight metal tube with its two curved branches made him think of a woman's figure. In a pile of odds and ends he found a square metal plaque which he attached to the top of the standing pipe. The plaque with its two holes for screws became the head with eyes. A piece of corrugated cardboard wrapped around the figure's torso made a pleated blouse, and a small fluted cake tin became a ruff around the woman's neck.

Anything could be used to make a piece of sculpture, Picasso believed, if it were used in the right way. "The king of rag pickers," Cocteau called him, because he picked up everything he found. A cake tin became a hat for a statue of a reaper, and a bicycle seat with handlebars made a bull's head with horns.

He also modeled a figure of a man holding a lamb. He made many drawings for this statue, until he pictured it so clearly in his mind that he was able to finish it in just one day. An aging man, seven feet tall, held a struggling lamb tightly in his arms. His bald head was thrust backwards as if to avoid the kicking beast.

All through the winter of 1944, Picasso modeled, drew and painted in his icy studio. Night after night, British planes bombed factories around Paris. Every day some friend was arrested by the Nazis, and then Picasso learned that Max Jacob had died in a German prison camp. Picasso was one of the few people who dared follow his Jewish friend to the cemetery.

In the spring, Parisians learned that American and British soldiers had landed on the coast of France. As the allied armies pushed on towards Paris, the Nazis fought back furiously. The sound of gunfire rattled the windows of Picasso's studio, but he continued to paint. At last, in August, the armies of liberation marched into Paris.

MAN WITH A LAMB

1944
Vallauris
Copyright SPADEM Paris

Reporters, art dealers and soldiers climbed the stairs to Picasso's studio. Pinned above the doorbell was a sign reading, "Here." Picasso, thin and lined, his white hair falling to his shoulders welcomed everyone who came.

Visitors noticed a tomato plant growing in his window. Picasso like other hungry Parisians grew vegetables on his balcony. He had painted the plant four times, he told his visitors.

"I have not painted the war," he said as he pulled out painting after painting, "but I have no doubt that the war is in these pictures I have made." There were lighted candles in many of the still lifes, for electricity had been scarce in war-time Paris. There were pictures of leeks, and another of a dead pigeon. He showed his visitors a painting of the buffet of the restaurant where he ate—a somber still life of artichokes and a sausage, the best food the owner was able to supply.

Six weeks after Paris was set free, a committee of artists organized a big exhibit. Picasso was given a special gallery in which to show his paintings and sculpture. Crowds poured into the gallery, curious to see how his work had changed during four years of war. Many people were shocked by the cheerless still lifes and the hideously distorted faces of the seated women. More were angered by a bicycle seat and handlebars which Picasso called a bull's head. Art students and elderly art lovers marched through the gallery shouting, "Take them down!" Some unhooked the canvases from the wall.

"These pictures are an insult to the intelligent public," a critic wrote and another protested that the paintings were more brutal than the horrors of the war.

"What do you think an artist is," Picasso wrote angrily in reply, "an imbecile who has only his eyes? . . . Painting is not to decorate apartments, it is an instrument of war for attack and defense against the enemy."

TOMATO PLANT

1944
Collection, Samuel Bronfman

Picasso soon tired of the visitors who poured into his studio, so in the spring of 1946 he set off for the south of France. The sun and sea filled him with renewed vigor. He longed to paint enormous canvases, he told the director of the museum in nearby Antibes; but, he complained, there was no room for big canvases in the house which a friend had loaned him. A few days later the director offered Picasso the top floor of his museum as a studio. Huge panels of sheet rock and cans of paint were moved into the old castle overlooking the sea. The director handed the keys of the castle to Picasso.

"There is a great lord who has found his place at last," he said, as Picasso closed the door behind him.

The sun shining through the shutters flooded the high-ceilinged rooms with a glowing light. Picasso, dressed in shorts and sandals, worked in peace. Piping fauns, dancing nymphs and capering goats came to life on the enormous panels. In one big picture, eight feet long, Picasso expressed his overflowing happiness. Against a background of transparent blue sea and sky a nude figure holding a tambourine, danced joyously. A centaur, half man, half horse, accompanied the dancer on a flute. An elongated faun whose tiny head reared high above the horizon played a pipe. Two kids, with human faces cavorted happily. Silhouetted against the sky was a ship with a yellow sail.

One day a friend, carrying a wounded owl, called at the workroom. Fascinated by its menacing eyes, which reminded him of his own, Picasso kept the bird beside him in a cage. Soon the glaring owl began to appear in his pictures.

When the winter wind started to blow through the unheated castle rooms Picasso stopped painting.

"I did what I could there and did it with pleasure," he told Sabartès.

Today Picasso's piping fauns, dancing nymphs and still lifes drenched in sunlight decorate the walls of the museum where Picasso painted for four months.

JOIE DE VIVRE

1946
Grimaldi Palace, Antibes
Photo Marianne Greenwood

Not far from Antibes was the village of Vallauris, a jumble of chimneys and red tiled roofs nestled in a valley of pine trees. Only a few of the chimneys were smoking in the summer of 1947, for the pottery business of Vallauris had failed.

During that summer, Picasso, curious to see how pottery was made, visited one of the workshops which was struggling to stay alive. Picking up a piece of clay he quickly modeled a figure of a bull. He loved the feel of the soft clay in his hands. The next day, dressed in shorts and sandals he visited the workshop again. Taking a bottle from the potter's wheel he laid it on its side. The craftsmen watched fascinated as he pinched the bottle's neck, gave it a few twists and suddenly the vase became a pigeon. Every day Picasso worked on new experiments. Under the pressure of his small firm hands a pitcher was turned into a duck, and a vase became a woman's figure with narrow waist and rounded hips.

He decorated the pieces with fascinating patterns. He painted goats' heads on plates, bullfighting scenes on platters and flowers on pitchers. He molded a six-handled vase into the shape of a frog, and he modeled many owls with bulging eyes and painted feathers.

In one year Picasso made two thousand different pieces. The craftsmen marveled that the strange shapes came out of the kiln unbroken. As each experiment succeeded, Picasso showed craftsmen how to copy his designs so that more people could buy his startling new ceramics.

Every day more craftsmen returned to work, more kilns were fired, and more of the Vallauris chimneys began to smoke.

OWL

1953
Painted Terra Cotta
From the Collection, Philip L. Goodwin

Picasso bought a little house on a hillside above Vallauris, so that he could be near the potter's workshop.

Every day buses roared into the central square of the little town bringing tourists who wanted to buy Picasso's pottery. As soon as the pieces which lined the store room shelves were sold, he designed new ones to replace them. From Paris came artists who were anxious to work in clay. The town barber, the baker and carpenter all visited the workshop, eager to learn the craft. Mothers came with their children who watched spellbound as Picasso decorated plates with drawings of animals and clown faces.

The people of Vallauris admired and loved the stocky, white-haired artist with coal black eyes, who had brought their town to life, and Picasso had a deep affection for the town which had offered him a field for new experiments. It was this town with red tiled roofs and tall smoking chimneys which he painted one day from his hillside home.

Picasso, wanting to express his gratitude to the people of Vallauris, decided to present a statue to the city council. He wanted it to be placed out doors, he told the mayor, where children could climb over it.

One day Picasso's bronze statue of the *Man with a Lamb* was brought from Paris and set up in the central square at Vallauris.

"This statue in our town will draw a new influx of visitors," wrote the editor of the Vallauris newspaper. "Picasso is not only a great artist, he is also a man with a heart."

SMOKE AT VALLAURIS

January 12, 1951
Collection the Artist

In an abandoned perfume factory which the town of Vallauris had offered him for a studio, Picasso found room to work on pieces of sculpture. He modeled figures in wet plaster, working with incredible speed before the plaster hardened. The odds and ends which he picked up in junk shops became parts of his sculpture.

"You should be able to pick up a piece of wood and find you have a bird in hand," he told a friend. A long-handled fork made a crane's foot, a child's shovel the tail. Its neck was a piece of metal cable and the crest the handle of an old faucet.

Every object which Picasso found he used in some surprising way. A child's ball became the body of an ape, a frying pan its tail, and a toy automobile its head.

On October twenty-fifth, 1951, the potters of Vallauris gave a birthday banquet for Picasso in a little chapel which had been deserted for many years. While speeches were made and poems were read, seventy-year-old Picasso examined the windowless walls which the town had asked him to decorate. He imagined the vaulted room covered with one enormous painting. On one side would be war and on the other peace.

The next spring two huge panels were installed in the perfume factory, while carpenters built a scaffolding on wheels.

"I must make *The Temple of Peace* now," he said to Kahnweiler, "while I am still able to climb a ladder."

No one saw the pictures Picasso was painting during the summer of 1952, but in the fall the doors of *The Temple of Peace* were opened and tourists streamed into the tiny chapel. An enormous picture, painted in brilliant colors, lighted up the cave-like vault. On one side Picasso had painted war. A horned figure in a chariot driven by black horses rumbled along a blood-red road. Against a grey background loomed shadows of five armed men. A figure holding a shield and spear stood calmly facing the attack. On the opposite wall was peace. A faun was piping, women were dancing and a child drove a winged horse which was attached to a plow.

BABOON AND YOUNG

1951
Collection Museum of Modern Art

Picasso returned to Paris in the fall of 1954, but he was constantly bothered by the stream of visitors that climbed the winding stairs to his studio. Finally in despair, he gave the studio to a friend and set off for the south of France.

He bought a spacious house surrounded by a high iron fence which stood on a hillside in Cannes. Soon the well-lighted rooms of *La Californie* were filled with crates of canvases, cartons of books and boxes of odds and ends which were never unpacked. From Boisgeloup came enormous bronzes which were set up in the tangled garden. He moved an engraver's press into one of the kitchens, and three big rooms on the ground floor became his studio. Here Picasso worked in peace.

The southern sun filtered by the shade of palm trees lighted up the cluttered rooms. He painted pictures of these rooms, creating restful patterns out of the disorder which he saw around him. In many of these pictures his beautiful dark-eyed friend Jacqueline sat in a rocking chair by a window. Over and over he painted portraits of Jacqueline, sometimes in Turkish dress, and sometimes he composed her portrait out of flat angular shapes which he painted with gay stripes. He painted her classical face on pieces of pottery and on heads which he built of flat metal cut-outs.

A film producer called at *La Californie* in the summer of 1955 and persuaded Picasso to allow himself to be photographed as he worked. Every day he would leave the cool quiet rooms of his home to paint in a moving-picture studio under the scorching heat of spotlights. Sweat poured down his neck and back, lines of fatigue marked his face, but his black eyes glowed as brilliantly as ever. Every few minutes the director interrupted Picasso's work so that his painting could be photographed. He covered canvas after canvas with drawings of nudes, still lifes, goats and bullfighters, and finally he painted an enormous picture of bathers. One steaming day he painted fourteen hours without stopping, until at last *The Mystery of Picasso* was finished. Overcome with exhaustion, Picasso was unable to paint for many weeks.

THE STUDIO

April 2, 1956
The Museum of Modern Art, New York

"If mirrors didn't exist I wouldn't know my age," he said.

Every time he sat at his easel he said to himself, "What can I teach myself today?"

Friends came and went from *La Californie*. Kahnweiler, Cocteau and Sabartès were always welcome. Almost every day Picasso received some artist, writer or musician.

Delegates from the United Nations called to ask Picasso to decorate a wall of the new UNESCO building in Paris. It was an enormous wall, thirty-three feet square.

"It can't be done," Picasso snapped, "I'm no longer twenty-five." Then as the delegates rose to go he turned to them suddenly.

"There is a solution," he said, "but I must find it myself."

Picasso painted the picture on forty separate panels. In the spring it was unveiled in the courtyard of the school at Vallauris. When the curtain was pulled aside, Picasso saw the assembled panels for the first time.

"Not bad," he remarked, "better than I thought."

A delegate explained the painting to the puzzled spectators. A spidery-looking object made of arms and legs was evil falling into darkness. On the left a female figure representing light ascended toward heaven. Three figures on the right symbolized humanity at peace.

While critics talked and wrote about his latest painting, seventy-eight-year-old Picasso was making new discoveries.

He bought a four-hundred-year-old castle, in the barren country of Vauvenargues, not far from Cannes. The windows looked out on rocky hills dotted with scrubby pines and on the red-tiled roofs of the town below.

"A real cubist village," Picasso said.

Carpenters and plumbers set to work putting in a furnace, but Picasso did not plan to live in this austere castle.

"Here I have settled with only my hat and shoes," he told a friend as he proudly showed him from room to room. "But," he said, his black eyes flashing, "wait and see what I'll paint on these bare walls."

MURAL PAINTING

1958
UNESCO Building, Paris
Photo Pierre Belzeaux

ACKNOWLEDGEMENTS

I wish to thank M. Jacques Dupiouy for procuring for me a photograph of *Man with a Lamb* and Marianne Greenwood for her kindness in sending me information about Picasso. I also wish to thank Mr. Frederick Rhinelander King for allowing me to reproduce a photograph of the terra cotta *owl*. I am most grateful for the help given me by Mr. Coman Leavenworth of the Library of the Museum of Modern Art in tracking down sources for photographs. I also wish to acknowledge thanks to M. Christian Zervos for allowing me to have copy negatives made of *La Malade* and New York Manager.

BIBLIOGRAPHY

Barr, Alfred H. Jr. *Picasso: Fifty Years of His Art*. The Museum of Modern Art, New York, 1946.

Beaumont, Cyril W. *The Diaghilev Ballet in London*. Putnam, London, 1940.

Cassou, Jean. *Picasso*. Translated from the French by Mary Chamont. The Art Book Publications. The Hyperion Press, London, New York, Paris, 1940.

Dale, Maud. *Picasso*. Alfred A. Knopf, New York, 1930.

Descargues, Pierre. *Picasso*. Témoins du XXe siècle. Editions Universitaires, Paris, 1956.

Duncan, David Douglas. *The Private World of Pablo Picasso*. Ridge Press, New York, 1958.

Elgar, Frank. *Picasso et Leger*. Les Amis de l'Art. Paris, 1954.

Elgar, Frank, and Maillard, Robert. *Picasso*. Translated from the French by Francis Scarfe. Frederick A. Praeger, New York, 1956.

Eluard, Paul. *Pablo Picasso*. Translated by Joseph T. Shipley. Philosophical Library, New York, 1947.

Eluard, Paul. *Picasso à Antibes*. Photographies de Michel Sima. René Drouin, Editeur, Paris, 1948.

Janis, Harriet and Sidney. *Picasso: The Recent Years, 1939-46*. Doubleday and Co., New York, 1946.

Kahnweiler, Daniel-Henry. *The Rise of Cubism*. Wittenborn, Schutz Inc., New York, 1949.

Kahnweiler, Daniel-Henry. *The Sculptures of Picasso*. Rodney Phillips & Co., London, 1949. (Photographs by Brassai).

Lieberman, William S. *Picasso. Blue and Rose Periods*. Art Treasures of the World, New York, An Abrams Book.

Larrea, Juan. *Guernica*. Curt Valentin, New York, 1947.

Leiris, Michel. *Picasso and the Human Comedy*. Harcourt, Brace and Company, New York, 1954.

Mackenzie, Helen I. *Understanding Picasso*. University of Chicago, Illinois, 1940.

Marrero, Vicente. *Picasso and the Bull*. Translated by Anthony Kerrigan. Henry Regnery Co., Chicago, 1956.

Melville, Robert. *Picasso: Master of the Phantom*. Oxford University Press, London, 1939.

Olivier, Fernande. *Picasso et Ses Amis*. Librairie Stock. Paris, 1933.

Penrose, Roland. *Portrait of Picasso*. Museum of Modern Art, New York, 1957.

Penrose, Roland. *Picasso: His Life and Work*. London, Victor Gollancz Ltd., 1958.

Picasso, Pablo. *Desire Trapped by the Tail*. Translated from the French by Bernard Frechtman. Philosophical Library, New York, 1948.

Picasso, Pablo. *Forty-nine Lithographs*. Lear Publishers, New York, 1947.

Picasso Libre. *21 Peintures, 1940-45*. Louis Carré, Paris, 1945.

Reverdy, Pierre. *Pablo Picasso et Son Oeuvre*. Editions de la Nouvelle Revue Française, Paris, 1924.

Roy, Claude. *Picasso—La Guerre et La Paix*. Editions Cercle d'Art, Paris, 1954.

Sabartès, Jaime. *Documents Iconographiques*. Pierre Cailler, Geneva, 1954.

Sabartès, Jaime. *An Intimate Portrait*. Translated from the Spanish by Angel Flores. Prentice-Hall, New York, 1948.

Stein, Gertrude. *Picasso*. London, B. T. Batsford, 1938.

Tzara, Tristan. *Picasso et les Chemins de la Connaissance*. Editions D'Art. Albert Skira, Geneva, 1948.

Uhde, Wilhelm. *Picasso et la Tradition Française*. Editions des Quatre-Chemins. Paris, 1928.

Vallentin, Antonina. *Pablo Picasso*. Editions Albin Michel, Paris, 1957.

Verdet, Andre. *L'Homme au Mouton*. Falaize, Paris, 1950.

Verdet, Andre. *Pablo Picasso au Musée d'Antibes*. Falaize, Paris, 1951.

Zervos, Christian. *Pablo Picasso*. In eight volumes. Editions "Cahiers d'Art," Paris, 1957.

INDEX